The
Midwife's
Journal

BIRTH LOG AND MEMORY BOOK

The
Midwife's
Journal

BIRTH LOG AND MEMORY BOOK

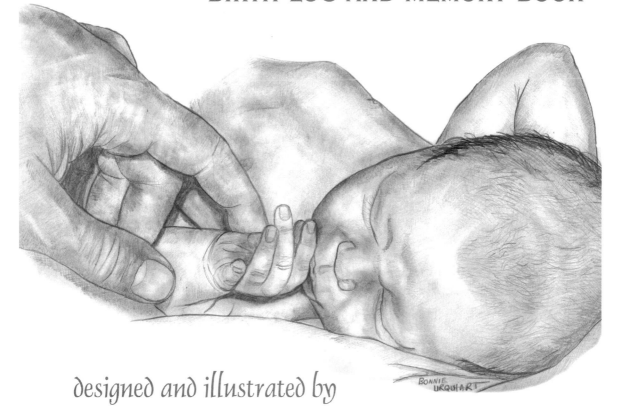

designed and illustrated by

BONNIE U. GRUENBERG CNM, MSN

 Birth Guru Publications • Duncannon, PA

The Midwife's Journal: Birth Log and Memory Book

Copyright © 2009 by Bonnie U. Gruenberg.

All illustrations © 2009 Bonnie U. Gruenberg.

Published by Birth Guru Publications

17 Pinetree Drive • Duncannon, PA 17020
To order, visit www.birthguru.com

Sources

Harman, J.H., & Kim, A. (1999). Current trends in cervical ripening and labor induction [Electronic version]. *American Family Physician 60*(2), 477–484. Retrieved February 15, 2009, from http://www.aafp.org/afp/990800ap/477.html

Summary of the New Ballard Score monograph. (n.d.). Retrieved February 15, 2009, from http://www.ballardscore.com/ScoreSheet.htm

Kramer, M.S., et al. (2001). A new and improved population-based Canadian reference for birthweight for gestational age [Electronic version]. *Pediatrics, 108*(2), e35. Retrieved February 15, 2009, from http: //www.pediatrics.org/cgi/content/full/108/2/e35

ISBN 13: 978-0-9790020-2-1   ISBN 10: 0-9790020-2-8

10   9   8   7   6   5   4   3   2   1

Also by Bonnie U. Gruenberg

Birth Emergency Skills Training: Manual for Out-of-Hospital Providers (Birth Guru, 2008)
Essentials of Prehospital Maternity Care (Prentice Hall, 2005)
Hoofprints in the Sand (Eclipse, 2002)

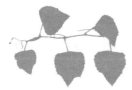

The author's paintings, drawings, and photographs, including those used in this book, are available as posters and giftware at www.birthguru.com.

Property of _____

Vaginal Births _____ through _____

Cesareans _____ through _____

Dates _____ through _____

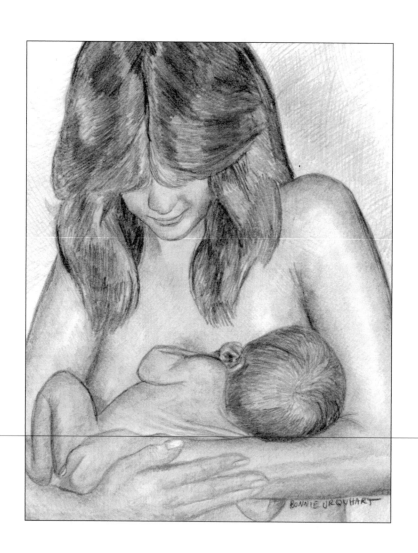

Every birth is a story. For years I have chronicled the stories of the births I have attended, preserving details against the passage of time and the imperfection of memory. Journals allow the stories to flow, but make it difficult to locate specifics at a moment's notice. Data logs are good for organizing and retrieving information essential to effective practice, but they are restrictive and often cramped or inadequate. As years passed and hundreds of babies slipped gently into my hands, I experimented with a variety of formats. Ultimately, I conceived a birth record that combines a journal and a data log in one convenient volume.

The Midwife's Journal accommodates the essential data for 100 vaginal births and 20 cesareans, which the practicing midwife can identify by name, number, or date. Generous margins and blank pages allow space for telling the story of each birth. A section for contact information and an appendix of forms and charts keep useful information close at hand. The one-of-a-kind freestyle index lets each user compile statistics or quickly refer to complicated cases or significant occurrences. This log will fit into a birth bag, and its durable binding will withstand daily use. And there is space on the spine for the midwife to identify and file each volume as the pages fill with memories.

I started my midwifery career in Erie, Pennsylvania, where vineyards cluster thickly along the lakeshore. While viticulturists nearby nurtured their vines from season to season and reaped bountiful harvests, babies were conceived, bellies blossomed, infants were born, and children grew. As I guided women to motherhood, their babies and children often found their way into my sketchpad. It seemed fitting to include their images in a journal that honors the stories of mothers and babies—stories that are profoundly unique, but in many respects always the same. Like the progression of seasons, life and birth continue.

Bonnie Urquhart Gruenberg

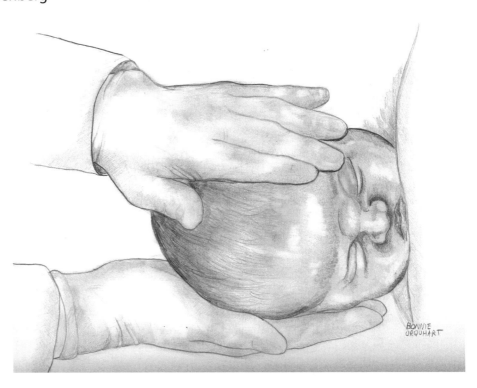

Date   Birth

MOTHER'S NAME AND ADDRESS		SIGNIFICANT HISTORY
G/P	**SUPPORT PERSONS**	**BIRTH STORY**
MATERNAL AGE		

MEDICATIONS AND INTERVENTIONS	LENGTH OF LABOR STAGES	APGARS AND WEIGHT
	LACERATIONS/EPISIOTOMY	BIRTH POSITION

BABY'S NAME	BABY'S SEX	TIME OF BIRTH
PLACE OF BIRTH	OTHERS IN ATTENDANCE	

THIRD AND FOURTH STAGES	POSTPARTUM	FEEDING

Date   Birth

MOTHER'S NAME AND ADDRESS		SIGNIFICANT HISTORY
G/P	**SUPPORT PERSONS**	**BIRTH STORY**
MATERNAL AGE		

MEDICATIONS AND INTERVENTIONS	LENGTH OF LABOR STAGES	APGARS AND WEIGHT
	LACERATIONS/EPISIOTOMY	BIRTH POSITION

BABY'S NAME	BABY'S SEX	TIME OF BIRTH
PLACE OF BIRTH	OTHERS IN ATTENDANCE	

THIRD AND FOURTH STAGES	POSTPARTUM	FEEDING

Birth

Date

MOTHER'S NAME AND ADDRESS		SIGNIFICANT HISTORY
G/P	**SUPPORT PERSONS**	**BIRTH STORY**
MATERNAL AGE		

MEDICATIONS AND INTERVENTIONS	LENGTH OF LABOR STAGES	APGARS AND WEIGHT
	LACERATIONS/EPISIOTOMY	BIRTH POSITION
BABY'S NAME	BABY'S SEX	TIME OF BIRTH
PLACE OF BIRTH	OTHERS IN ATTENDANCE	

THIRD AND FOURTH STAGES	POSTPARTUM	FEEDING

Birth

Date

MOTHER'S NAME AND ADDRESS		SIGNIFICANT HISTORY
G/P	**SUPPORT PERSONS**	**BIRTH STORY**
MATERNAL AGE		

MEDICATIONS AND INTERVENTIONS	LENGTH OF LABOR STAGES	APGARS AND WEIGHT
	LACERATIONS/EPISIOTOMY	BIRTH POSITION
BABY'S NAME	BABY'S SEX	TIME OF BIRTH
PLACE OF BIRTH	OTHERS IN ATTENDANCE	

THIRD AND FOURTH STAGES	POSTPARTUM	FEEDING

Date   Birth #

MOTHER'S NAME AND ADDRESS		SIGNIFICANT HISTORY	
G/P	SUPPORT PERSONS	BIRTH STORY	
MATERNAL AGE			

MEDICATIONS AND INTERVENTIONS	LENGTH OF LABOR STAGES	APGARS AND WEIGHT
	LACERATIONS/EPISIOTOMY	BIRTH POSITION

BABY'S NAME	BABY'S SEX	TIME OF BIRTH
PLACE OF BIRTH	OTHERS IN ATTENDANCE	

THIRD AND FOURTH STAGES	POSTPARTUM	FEEDING

Date   Birth #

MOTHER'S NAME AND ADDRESS		SIGNIFICANT HISTORY	
G/P	SUPPORT PERSONS	BIRTH STORY	
MATERNAL AGE			

MEDICATIONS AND INTERVENTIONS	LENGTH OF LABOR STAGES	APGARS AND WEIGHT
	LACERATIONS/EPISIOTOMY	BIRTH POSITION

BABY'S NAME	BABY'S SEX	TIME OF BIRTH
PLACE OF BIRTH	OTHERS IN ATTENDANCE	

THIRD AND FOURTH STAGES	POSTPARTUM	FEEDING

II

Birth

Date

MOTHER'S NAME AND ADDRESS

SIGNIFICANT HISTORY

G/P

SUPPORT PERSONS

MATERNAL AGE

BIRTH STORY

MEDICATIONS AND INTERVENTIONS

LENGTH OF LABOR STAGES

APGARS AND WEIGHT

LACERATIONS/EPISIOTOMY

BIRTH POSITION

BABY'S NAME

BABY'S SEX

TIME OF BIRTH

PLACE OF BIRTH

OTHERS IN ATTENDANCE

THIRD AND FOURTH STAGES

POSTPARTUM

FEEDING

Birth

Date

MOTHER'S NAME AND ADDRESS

SIGNIFICANT HISTORY

G/P

SUPPORT PERSONS

MATERNAL AGE

BIRTH STORY

MEDICATIONS AND INTERVENTIONS

LENGTH OF LABOR STAGES

APGARS AND WEIGHT

LACERATIONS/EPISIOTOMY

BIRTH POSITION

BABY'S NAME

BABY'S SEX

TIME OF BIRTH

PLACE OF BIRTH

OTHERS IN ATTENDANCE

THIRD AND FOURTH STAGES

POSTPARTUM

FEEDING

Date   Birth

MOTHER'S NAME AND ADDRESS		SIGNIFICANT HISTORY	
G/P	**SUPPORT PERSONS**	**BIRTH STORY**	
MATERNAL AGE			

MEDICATIONS AND INTERVENTIONS	LENGTH OF LABOR STAGES	APGARS AND WEIGHT
	LACERATIONS/EPISIOTOMY	BIRTH POSITION

BABY'S NAME	BABY'S SEX	TIME OF BIRTH
PLACE OF BIRTH	OTHERS IN ATTENDANCE	

THIRD AND FOURTH STAGES	POSTPARTUM	FEEDING

Date   Birth

MOTHER'S NAME AND ADDRESS		SIGNIFICANT HISTORY	
G/P	**SUPPORT PERSONS**	**BIRTH STORY**	
MATERNAL AGE			

MEDICATIONS AND INTERVENTIONS	LENGTH OF LABOR STAGES	APGARS AND WEIGHT
	LACERATIONS/EPISIOTOMY	BIRTH POSITION

BABY'S NAME	BABY'S SEX	TIME OF BIRTH
PLACE OF BIRTH	OTHERS IN ATTENDANCE	

THIRD AND FOURTH STAGES	POSTPARTUM	FEEDING

Birth

Date

MOTHER'S NAME AND ADDRESS		SIGNIFICANT HISTORY
G/P	SUPPORT PERSONS	BIRTH STORY
MATERNAL AGE		

MEDICATIONS AND INTERVENTIONS	LENGTH OF LABOR STAGES	APGARS AND WEIGHT
	LACERATIONS/EPISIOTOMY	BIRTH POSITION

BABY'S NAME	BABY'S SEX	TIME OF BIRTH
PLACE OF BIRTH	OTHERS IN ATTENDANCE	

THIRD AND FOURTH STAGES	POSTPARTUM	FEEDING

Birth

Date

MOTHER'S NAME AND ADDRESS		SIGNIFICANT HISTORY
G/P	SUPPORT PERSONS	BIRTH STORY
MATERNAL AGE		

MEDICATIONS AND INTERVENTIONS	LENGTH OF LABOR STAGES	APGARS AND WEIGHT
	LACERATIONS/EPISIOTOMY	BIRTH POSITION

BABY'S NAME	BABY'S SEX	TIME OF BIRTH
PLACE OF BIRTH	OTHERS IN ATTENDANCE	

THIRD AND FOURTH STAGES	POSTPARTUM	FEEDING

Date   Birth #

MOTHER'S NAME AND ADDRESS		SIGNIFICANT HISTORY	
G/P	SUPPORT PERSONS	BIRTH STORY	
MATERNAL AGE			
MEDICATIONS AND INTERVENTIONS	LENGTH OF LABOR STAGES		APGARS AND WEIGHT
	LACERATIONS/EPISIOTOMY		BIRTH POSITION
BABY'S NAME		BABY'S SEX	TIME OF BIRTH
PLACE OF BIRTH		OTHERS IN ATTENDANCE	
THIRD AND FOURTH STAGES	POSTPARTUM		FEEDING

Date   Birth #

MOTHER'S NAME AND ADDRESS		SIGNIFICANT HISTORY	
G/P	SUPPORT PERSONS	BIRTH STORY	
MATERNAL AGE			
MEDICATIONS AND INTERVENTIONS	LENGTH OF LABOR STAGES		APGARS AND WEIGHT
	LACERATIONS/EPISIOTOMY		BIRTH POSITION
BABY'S NAME		BABY'S SEX	TIME OF BIRTH
PLACE OF BIRTH		OTHERS IN ATTENDANCE	
THIRD AND FOURTH STAGES	POSTPARTUM		FEEDING

Birth #   Date

MOTHER'S NAME AND ADDRESS			SIGNIFICANT HISTORY	
G/P	SUPPORT PERSONS		BIRTH STORY	
MATERNAL AGE				
MEDICATIONS AND INTERVENTIONS		LENGTH OF LABOR STAGES		APGARS AND WEIGHT
		LACERATIONS/EPISIOTOMY		BIRTH POSITION
BABY'S NAME			BABY'S SEX	TIME OF BIRTH
PLACE OF BIRTH			OTHERS IN ATTENDANCE	
THIRD AND FOURTH STAGES		POSTPARTUM		FEEDING

Birth #   Date

MOTHER'S NAME AND ADDRESS			SIGNIFICANT HISTORY	
G/P	SUPPORT PERSONS		BIRTH STORY	
MATERNAL AGE				
MEDICATIONS AND INTERVENTIONS		LENGTH OF LABOR STAGES		APGARS AND WEIGHT
		LACERATIONS/EPISIOTOMY		BIRTH POSITION
BABY'S NAME			BABY'S SEX	TIME OF BIRTH
PLACE OF BIRTH			OTHERS IN ATTENDANCE	
THIRD AND FOURTH STAGES		POSTPARTUM		FEEDING

Date   Birth

MOTHER'S NAME AND ADDRESS		SIGNIFICANT HISTORY
G/P	**SUPPORT PERSONS**	**BIRTH STORY**
MATERNAL AGE		

MEDICATIONS AND INTERVENTIONS	LENGTH OF LABOR STAGES	APGARS AND WEIGHT
	LACERATIONS/EPISIOTOMY	BIRTH POSITION
BABY'S NAME	**BABY'S SEX**	**TIME OF BIRTH**
PLACE OF BIRTH	**OTHERS IN ATTENDANCE**	

THIRD AND FOURTH STAGES	POSTPARTUM	FEEDING

Date   Birth

MOTHER'S NAME AND ADDRESS		SIGNIFICANT HISTORY
G/P	**SUPPORT PERSONS**	**BIRTH STORY**
MATERNAL AGE		

MEDICATIONS AND INTERVENTIONS	LENGTH OF LABOR STAGES	APGARS AND WEIGHT
	LACERATIONS/EPISIOTOMY	BIRTH POSITION
BABY'S NAME	**BABY'S SEX**	**TIME OF BIRTH**
PLACE OF BIRTH	**OTHERS IN ATTENDANCE**	

THIRD AND FOURTH STAGES	POSTPARTUM	FEEDING

Birth #   Date

MOTHER'S NAME AND ADDRESS			SIGNIFICANT HISTORY	
G/P	**SUPPORT PERSONS**		**BIRTH STORY**	
MATERNAL AGE				
MEDICATIONS AND INTERVENTIONS	LENGTH OF LABOR STAGES		APGARS AND WEIGHT	
	LACERATIONS/EPISIOTOMY		BIRTH POSITION	
BABY'S NAME		BABY'S SEX		TIME OF BIRTH
PLACE OF BIRTH		OTHERS IN ATTENDANCE		
THIRD AND FOURTH STAGES	POSTPARTUM		FEEDING	

Birth #   Date

MOTHER'S NAME AND ADDRESS			SIGNIFICANT HISTORY	
G/P	**SUPPORT PERSONS**		**BIRTH STORY**	
MATERNAL AGE				
MEDICATIONS AND INTERVENTIONS	LENGTH OF LABOR STAGES		APGARS AND WEIGHT	
	LACERATIONS/EPISIOTOMY		BIRTH POSITION	
BABY'S NAME		BABY'S SEX		TIME OF BIRTH
PLACE OF BIRTH		OTHERS IN ATTENDANCE		
THIRD AND FOURTH STAGES	POSTPARTUM		FEEDING	

Notes

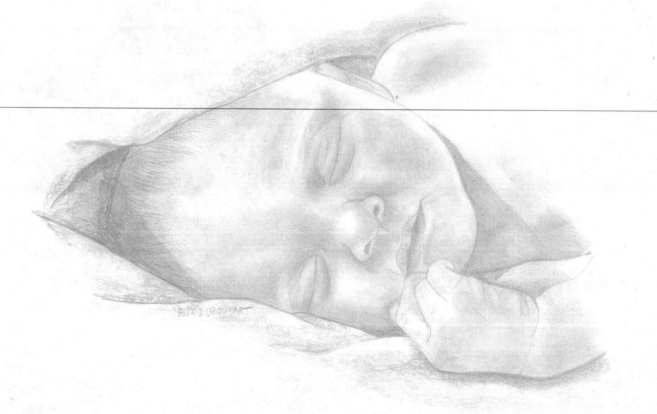

Date   Birth

MOTHER'S NAME AND ADDRESS		SIGNIFICANT HISTORY	

G/P	SUPPORT PERSONS	BIRTH STORY	
MATERNAL AGE			

MEDICATIONS AND INTERVENTIONS	LENGTH OF LABOR STAGES	APGARS AND WEIGHT
	LACERATIONS/EPISIOTOMY	BIRTH POSITION

BABY'S NAME	BABY'S SEX	TIME OF BIRTH
PLACE OF BIRTH	OTHERS IN ATTENDANCE	

THIRD AND FOURTH STAGES	POSTPARTUM	FEEDING

Date   Birth

MOTHER'S NAME AND ADDRESS		SIGNIFICANT HISTORY	

G/P	SUPPORT PERSONS	BIRTH STORY	
MATERNAL AGE			

MEDICATIONS AND INTERVENTIONS	LENGTH OF LABOR STAGES	APGARS AND WEIGHT
	LACERATIONS/EPISIOTOMY	BIRTH POSITION

BABY'S NAME	BABY'S SEX	TIME OF BIRTH
PLACE OF BIRTH	OTHERS IN ATTENDANCE	

THIRD AND FOURTH STAGES	POSTPARTUM	FEEDING

Birth

Date

MOTHER'S NAME AND ADDRESS		SIGNIFICANT HISTORY
G/P	SUPPORT PERSONS	BIRTH STORY
MATERNAL AGE		

MEDICATIONS AND INTERVENTIONS	LENGTH OF LABOR STAGES	APGARS AND WEIGHT
	LACERATIONS/EPISIOTOMY	BIRTH POSITION
BABY'S NAME	BABY'S SEX	TIME OF BIRTH
PLACE OF BIRTH	OTHERS IN ATTENDANCE	

THIRD AND FOURTH STAGES	POSTPARTUM	FEEDING

Birth

Date

MOTHER'S NAME AND ADDRESS		SIGNIFICANT HISTORY
G/P	SUPPORT PERSONS	BIRTH STORY
MATERNAL AGE		

MEDICATIONS AND INTERVENTIONS	LENGTH OF LABOR STAGES	APGARS AND WEIGHT
	LACERATIONS/EPISIOTOMY	BIRTH POSITION
BABY'S NAME	BABY'S SEX	TIME OF BIRTH
PLACE OF BIRTH	OTHERS IN ATTENDANCE	

THIRD AND FOURTH STAGES	POSTPARTUM	FEEDING

Date

Birth

MOTHER'S NAME AND ADDRESS	SIGNIFICANT HISTORY

G/P	SUPPORT PERSONS	BIRTH STORY
MATERNAL AGE		

MEDICATIONS AND INTERVENTIONS	LENGTH OF LABOR STAGES	APGARS AND WEIGHT
	LACERATIONS/EPISIOTOMY	BIRTH POSITION

BABY'S NAME	BABY'S SEX	TIME OF BIRTH

PLACE OF BIRTH	OTHERS IN ATTENDANCE

THIRD AND FOURTH STAGES	POSTPARTUM	FEEDING

Date

Birth

MOTHER'S NAME AND ADDRESS	SIGNIFICANT HISTORY

G/P	SUPPORT PERSONS	BIRTH STORY
MATERNAL AGE		

MEDICATIONS AND INTERVENTIONS	LENGTH OF LABOR STAGES	APGARS AND WEIGHT
	LACERATIONS/EPISIOTOMY	BIRTH POSITION

BABY'S NAME	BABY'S SEX	TIME OF BIRTH

PLACE OF BIRTH	OTHERS IN ATTENDANCE

THIRD AND FOURTH STAGES	POSTPARTUM	FEEDING

Birth

Date

MOTHER'S NAME AND ADDRESS	SIGNIFICANT HISTORY

G/P	SUPPORT PERSONS	BIRTH STORY
MATERNAL AGE		

MEDICATIONS AND INTERVENTIONS	LENGTH OF LABOR STAGES	APGARS AND WEIGHT
	LACERATIONS/EPISIOTOMY	BIRTH POSITION

BABY'S NAME	BABY'S SEX	TIME OF BIRTH

PLACE OF BIRTH	OTHERS IN ATTENDANCE

THIRD AND FOURTH STAGES	POSTPARTUM	FEEDING

Birth

Date

MOTHER'S NAME AND ADDRESS	SIGNIFICANT HISTORY

G/P	SUPPORT PERSONS	BIRTH STORY
MATERNAL AGE		

MEDICATIONS AND INTERVENTIONS	LENGTH OF LABOR STAGES	APGARS AND WEIGHT
	LACERATIONS/EPISIOTOMY	BIRTH POSITION

BABY'S NAME	BABY'S SEX	TIME OF BIRTH

PLACE OF BIRTH	OTHERS IN ATTENDANCE

THIRD AND FOURTH STAGES	POSTPARTUM	FEEDING

Date   Birth

MOTHER'S NAME AND ADDRESS	SIGNIFICANT HISTORY

G/P	SUPPORT PERSONS	BIRTH STORY
MATERNAL AGE		

MEDICATIONS AND INTERVENTIONS	LENGTH OF LABOR STAGES	APGARS AND WEIGHT
	LACERATIONS/EPISIOTOMY	BIRTH POSITION

BABY'S NAME	BABY'S SEX	TIME OF BIRTH
PLACE OF BIRTH	OTHERS IN ATTENDANCE	

THIRD AND FOURTH STAGES	POSTPARTUM	FEEDING

Date   Birth

MOTHER'S NAME AND ADDRESS	SIGNIFICANT HISTORY

G/P	SUPPORT PERSONS	BIRTH STORY
MATERNAL AGE		

MEDICATIONS AND INTERVENTIONS	LENGTH OF LABOR STAGES	APGARS AND WEIGHT
	LACERATIONS/EPISIOTOMY	BIRTH POSITION

BABY'S NAME	BABY'S SEX	TIME OF BIRTH
PLACE OF BIRTH	OTHERS IN ATTENDANCE	

THIRD AND FOURTH STAGES	POSTPARTUM	FEEDING

Birth #   Date

MOTHER'S NAME AND ADDRESS		SIGNIFICANT HISTORY	

G/P	SUPPORT PERSONS	BIRTH STORY	
MATERNAL AGE			

MEDICATIONS AND INTERVENTIONS	LENGTH OF LABOR STAGES	APGARS AND WEIGHT
	LACERATIONS/EPISIOTOMY	BIRTH POSITION

BABY'S NAME	BABY'S SEX	TIME OF BIRTH
PLACE OF BIRTH	OTHERS IN ATTENDANCE	

THIRD AND FOURTH STAGES	POSTPARTUM	FEEDING

Birth #   Date

MOTHER'S NAME AND ADDRESS		SIGNIFICANT HISTORY	

G/P	SUPPORT PERSONS	BIRTH STORY	
MATERNAL AGE			

MEDICATIONS AND INTERVENTIONS	LENGTH OF LABOR STAGES	APGARS AND WEIGHT
	LACERATIONS/EPISIOTOMY	BIRTH POSITION

BABY'S NAME	BABY'S SEX	TIME OF BIRTH
PLACE OF BIRTH	OTHERS IN ATTENDANCE	

THIRD AND FOURTH STAGES	POSTPARTUM	FEEDING

Date

Birth

MOTHER'S NAME AND ADDRESS	SIGNIFICANT HISTORY

G/P	SUPPORT PERSONS	BIRTH STORY
MATERNAL AGE		

MEDICATIONS AND INTERVENTIONS	LENGTH OF LABOR STAGES	APGARS AND WEIGHT
	LACERATIONS/EPISIOTOMY	BIRTH POSITION

BABY'S NAME	BABY'S SEX	TIME OF BIRTH

PLACE OF BIRTH	OTHERS IN ATTENDANCE

THIRD AND FOURTH STAGES	POSTPARTUM	FEEDING

Date

Birth

MOTHER'S NAME AND ADDRESS	SIGNIFICANT HISTORY

G/P	SUPPORT PERSONS	BIRTH STORY
MATERNAL AGE		

MEDICATIONS AND INTERVENTIONS	LENGTH OF LABOR STAGES	APGARS AND WEIGHT
	LACERATIONS/EPISIOTOMY	BIRTH POSITION

BABY'S NAME	BABY'S SEX	TIME OF BIRTH

PLACE OF BIRTH	OTHERS IN ATTENDANCE

THIRD AND FOURTH STAGES	POSTPARTUM	FEEDING

Birth

Date

MOTHER'S NAME AND ADDRESS	SIGNIFICANT HISTORY

G/P	SUPPORT PERSONS	BIRTH STORY
MATERNAL AGE		

MEDICATIONS AND INTERVENTIONS	LENGTH OF LABOR STAGES	APGARS AND WEIGHT
	LACERATIONS/EPISIOTOMY	BIRTH POSITION

BABY'S NAME	BABY'S SEX	TIME OF BIRTH
PLACE OF BIRTH	OTHERS IN ATTENDANCE	

THIRD AND FOURTH STAGES	POSTPARTUM	FEEDING

Birth

Date

MOTHER'S NAME AND ADDRESS	SIGNIFICANT HISTORY

G/P	SUPPORT PERSONS	BIRTH STORY
MATERNAL AGE		

MEDICATIONS AND INTERVENTIONS	LENGTH OF LABOR STAGES	APGARS AND WEIGHT
	LACERATIONS/EPISIOTOMY	BIRTH POSITION

BABY'S NAME	BABY'S SEX	TIME OF BIRTH
PLACE OF BIRTH	OTHERS IN ATTENDANCE	

THIRD AND FOURTH STAGES	POSTPARTUM	FEEDING

Date   Birth

MOTHER'S NAME AND ADDRESS		SIGNIFICANT HISTORY

G/P	SUPPORT PERSONS	BIRTH STORY
MATERNAL AGE		

MEDICATIONS AND INTERVENTIONS	LENGTH OF LABOR STAGES	APGARS AND WEIGHT
	LACERATIONS/EPISIOTOMY	BIRTH POSITION

BABY'S NAME	BABY'S SEX	TIME OF BIRTH
PLACE OF BIRTH	OTHERS IN ATTENDANCE	

THIRD AND FOURTH STAGES	POSTPARTUM	FEEDING

Date   Birth

MOTHER'S NAME AND ADDRESS		SIGNIFICANT HISTORY

G/P	SUPPORT PERSONS	BIRTH STORY
MATERNAL AGE		

MEDICATIONS AND INTERVENTIONS	LENGTH OF LABOR STAGES	APGARS AND WEIGHT
	LACERATIONS/EPISIOTOMY	BIRTH POSITION

BABY'S NAME	BABY'S SEX	TIME OF BIRTH
PLACE OF BIRTH	OTHERS IN ATTENDANCE	

THIRD AND FOURTH STAGES	POSTPARTUM	FEEDING

Birth #   Date

MOTHER'S NAME AND ADDRESS		SIGNIFICANT HISTORY	

G/P	SUPPORT PERSONS	BIRTH STORY	
MATERNAL AGE			

MEDICATIONS AND INTERVENTIONS	LENGTH OF LABOR STAGES	APGARS AND WEIGHT
	LACERATIONS/EPISIOTOMY	BIRTH POSITION

BABY'S NAME	BABY'S SEX	TIME OF BIRTH
PLACE OF BIRTH	OTHERS IN ATTENDANCE	

THIRD AND FOURTH STAGES	POSTPARTUM	FEEDING

Birth #   Date

MOTHER'S NAME AND ADDRESS		SIGNIFICANT HISTORY	

G/P	SUPPORT PERSONS	BIRTH STORY	
MATERNAL AGE			

MEDICATIONS AND INTERVENTIONS	LENGTH OF LABOR STAGES	APGARS AND WEIGHT
	LACERATIONS/EPISIOTOMY	BIRTH POSITION

BABY'S NAME	BABY'S SEX	TIME OF BIRTH
PLACE OF BIRTH	OTHERS IN ATTENDANCE	

THIRD AND FOURTH STAGES	POSTPARTUM	FEEDING

 Memories

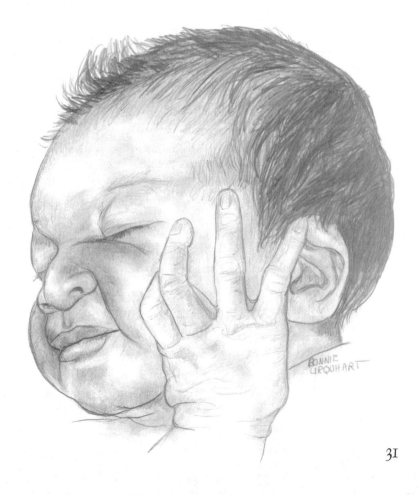

BONNIE URQUHART

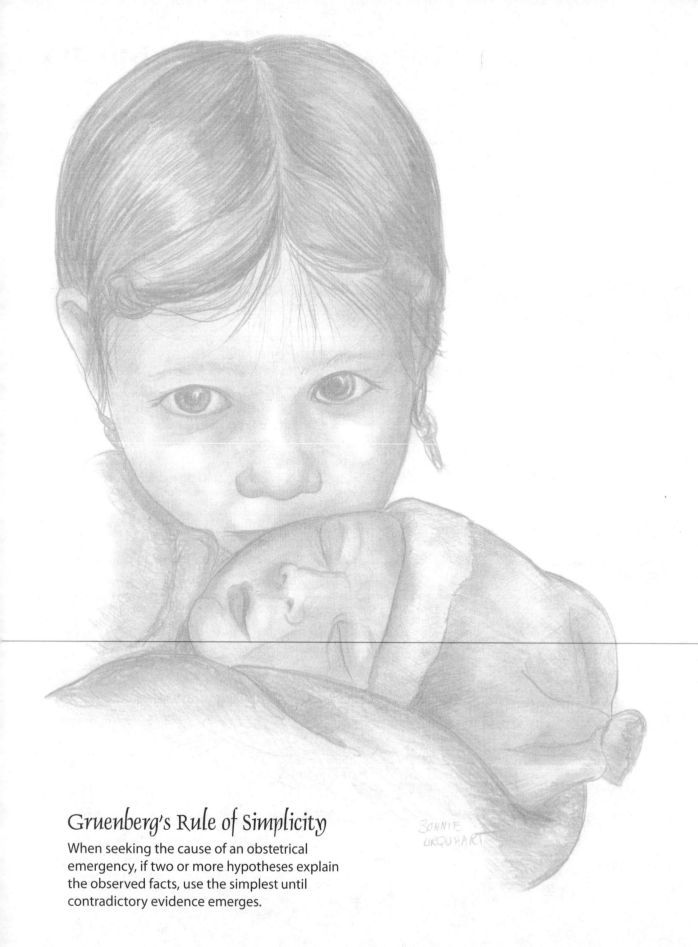

Gruenberg's Rule of Simplicity

When seeking the cause of an obstetrical
emergency, if two or more hypotheses explain
the observed facts, use the simplest until
contradictory evidence emerges.

BONNIE
URQUHART

32

Date

Birth

MOTHER'S NAME AND ADDRESS	SIGNIFICANT HISTORY

G/P	SUPPORT PERSONS	BIRTH STORY
MATERNAL AGE		

MEDICATIONS AND INTERVENTIONS	LENGTH OF LABOR STAGES	APGARS AND WEIGHT
	LACERATIONS/EPISIOTOMY	BIRTH POSITION

BABY'S NAME	BABY'S SEX	TIME OF BIRTH
PLACE OF BIRTH	OTHERS IN ATTENDANCE	

THIRD AND FOURTH STAGES	POSTPARTUM	FEEDING

Date

Birth

MOTHER'S NAME AND ADDRESS	SIGNIFICANT HISTORY

G/P	SUPPORT PERSONS	BIRTH STORY
MATERNAL AGE		

MEDICATIONS AND INTERVENTIONS	LENGTH OF LABOR STAGES	APGARS AND WEIGHT
	LACERATIONS/EPISIOTOMY	BIRTH POSITION

BABY'S NAME	BABY'S SEX	TIME OF BIRTH
PLACE OF BIRTH	OTHERS IN ATTENDANCE	

THIRD AND FOURTH STAGES	POSTPARTUM	FEEDING

Birth #   Date

MOTHER'S NAME AND ADDRESS		SIGNIFICANT HISTORY

G/P	SUPPORT PERSONS	BIRTH STORY
MATERNAL AGE		

MEDICATIONS AND INTERVENTIONS	LENGTH OF LABOR STAGES	APGARS AND WEIGHT
	LACERATIONS/EPISIOTOMY	BIRTH POSITION

BABY'S NAME	BABY'S SEX	TIME OF BIRTH
PLACE OF BIRTH	OTHERS IN ATTENDANCE	

THIRD AND FOURTH STAGES	POSTPARTUM	FEEDING

Birth #   Date

MOTHER'S NAME AND ADDRESS		SIGNIFICANT HISTORY

G/P	SUPPORT PERSONS	BIRTH STORY
MATERNAL AGE		

MEDICATIONS AND INTERVENTIONS	LENGTH OF LABOR STAGES	APGARS AND WEIGHT
	LACERATIONS/EPISIOTOMY	BIRTH POSITION

BABY'S NAME	BABY'S SEX	TIME OF BIRTH
PLACE OF BIRTH	OTHERS IN ATTENDANCE	

THIRD AND FOURTH STAGES	POSTPARTUM	FEEDING

MOTHER'S NAME AND ADDRESS

SIGNIFICANT HISTORY

G/P

SUPPORT PERSONS

BIRTH STORY

MATERNAL AGE

MEDICATIONS AND INTERVENTIONS

LENGTH OF LABOR STAGES

APGARS AND WEIGHT

LACERATIONS/EPISIOTOMY

BIRTH POSITION

BABY'S NAME

BABY'S SEX

TIME OF BIRTH

PLACE OF BIRTH

OTHERS IN ATTENDANCE

THIRD AND FOURTH STAGES

POSTPARTUM

FEEDING

Date   Birth #

MOTHER'S NAME AND ADDRESS

SIGNIFICANT HISTORY

G/P

SUPPORT PERSONS

BIRTH STORY

MATERNAL AGE

MEDICATIONS AND INTERVENTIONS

LENGTH OF LABOR STAGES

APGARS AND WEIGHT

LACERATIONS/EPISIOTOMY

BIRTH POSITION

BABY'S NAME

BABY'S SEX

TIME OF BIRTH

PLACE OF BIRTH

OTHERS IN ATTENDANCE

THIRD AND FOURTH STAGES

POSTPARTUM

FEEDING

Birth

Date

MOTHER'S NAME AND ADDRESS		SIGNIFICANT HISTORY
G/P	**SUPPORT PERSONS**	**BIRTH STORY**
MATERNAL AGE		

MEDICATIONS AND INTERVENTIONS	LENGTH OF LABOR STAGES	APGARS AND WEIGHT
	LACERATIONS/EPISIOTOMY	BIRTH POSITION

BABY'S NAME	BABY'S SEX	TIME OF BIRTH
PLACE OF BIRTH	OTHERS IN ATTENDANCE	

THIRD AND FOURTH STAGES	POSTPARTUM	FEEDING

Birth

Date

MOTHER'S NAME AND ADDRESS		SIGNIFICANT HISTORY
G/P	**SUPPORT PERSONS**	**BIRTH STORY**
MATERNAL AGE		

MEDICATIONS AND INTERVENTIONS	LENGTH OF LABOR STAGES	APGARS AND WEIGHT
	LACERATIONS/EPISIOTOMY	BIRTH POSITION

BABY'S NAME	BABY'S SEX	TIME OF BIRTH
PLACE OF BIRTH	OTHERS IN ATTENDANCE	

THIRD AND FOURTH STAGES	POSTPARTUM	FEEDING

Date

Birth

MOTHER'S NAME AND ADDRESS		SIGNIFICANT HISTORY	
G/P	SUPPORT PERSONS	BIRTH STORY	
MATERNAL AGE			
MEDICATIONS AND INTERVENTIONS	LENGTH OF LABOR STAGES	APGARS AND WEIGHT	
	LACERATIONS/EPISIOTOMY	BIRTH POSITION	
BABY'S NAME		BABY'S SEX	TIME OF BIRTH
PLACE OF BIRTH		OTHERS IN ATTENDANCE	
THIRD AND FOURTH STAGES	POSTPARTUM		FEEDING

Date

Birth

MOTHER'S NAME AND ADDRESS		SIGNIFICANT HISTORY	
G/P	SUPPORT PERSONS	BIRTH STORY	
MATERNAL AGE			
MEDICATIONS AND INTERVENTIONS	LENGTH OF LABOR STAGES	APGARS AND WEIGHT	
	LACERATIONS/EPISIOTOMY	BIRTH POSITION	
BABY'S NAME		BABY'S SEX	TIME OF BIRTH
PLACE OF BIRTH		OTHERS IN ATTENDANCE	
THIRD AND FOURTH STAGES	POSTPARTUM		FEEDING

Birth #   Date

MOTHER'S NAME AND ADDRESS		SIGNIFICANT HISTORY
G/P	SUPPORT PERSONS	BIRTH STORY
MATERNAL AGE		

MEDICATIONS AND INTERVENTIONS	LENGTH OF LABOR STAGES	APGARS AND WEIGHT
	LACERATIONS/EPISIOTOMY	BIRTH POSITION

BABY'S NAME	BABY'S SEX	TIME OF BIRTH
PLACE OF BIRTH	OTHERS IN ATTENDANCE	

THIRD AND FOURTH STAGES	POSTPARTUM	FEEDING

Birth #   Date

MOTHER'S NAME AND ADDRESS		SIGNIFICANT HISTORY
G/P	SUPPORT PERSONS	BIRTH STORY
MATERNAL AGE		

MEDICATIONS AND INTERVENTIONS	LENGTH OF LABOR STAGES	APGARS AND WEIGHT
	LACERATIONS/EPISIOTOMY	BIRTH POSITION

BABY'S NAME	BABY'S SEX	TIME OF BIRTH
PLACE OF BIRTH	OTHERS IN ATTENDANCE	

THIRD AND FOURTH STAGES	POSTPARTUM	FEEDING

Date   Birth

MOTHER'S NAME AND ADDRESS	SIGNIFICANT HISTORY

G/P	SUPPORT PERSONS	BIRTH STORY
MATERNAL AGE		

MEDICATIONS AND INTERVENTIONS	LENGTH OF LABOR STAGES	APGARS AND WEIGHT
	LACERATIONS/EPISIOTOMY	BIRTH POSITION

BABY'S NAME	BABY'S SEX	TIME OF BIRTH
PLACE OF BIRTH	OTHERS IN ATTENDANCE	

THIRD AND FOURTH STAGES	POSTPARTUM	FEEDING

Date   Birth

MOTHER'S NAME AND ADDRESS	SIGNIFICANT HISTORY

G/P	SUPPORT PERSONS	BIRTH STORY
MATERNAL AGE		

MEDICATIONS AND INTERVENTIONS	LENGTH OF LABOR STAGES	APGARS AND WEIGHT
	LACERATIONS/EPISIOTOMY	BIRTH POSITION

BABY'S NAME	BABY'S SEX	TIME OF BIRTH
PLACE OF BIRTH	OTHERS IN ATTENDANCE	

THIRD AND FOURTH STAGES	POSTPARTUM	FEEDING

Birth #   Date

MOTHER'S NAME AND ADDRESS		SIGNIFICANT HISTORY	
G/P	SUPPORT PERSONS	BIRTH STORY	
MATERNAL AGE			

MEDICATIONS AND INTERVENTIONS	LENGTH OF LABOR STAGES		APGARS AND WEIGHT
	LACERATIONS/EPISIOTOMY		BIRTH POSITION
BABY'S NAME		BABY'S SEX	TIME OF BIRTH
PLACE OF BIRTH		OTHERS IN ATTENDANCE	
THIRD AND FOURTH STAGES	POSTPARTUM		FEEDING

Birth #   Date

MOTHER'S NAME AND ADDRESS		SIGNIFICANT HISTORY	
G/P	SUPPORT PERSONS	BIRTH STORY	
MATERNAL AGE			

MEDICATIONS AND INTERVENTIONS	LENGTH OF LABOR STAGES		APGARS AND WEIGHT
	LACERATIONS/EPISIOTOMY		BIRTH POSITION
BABY'S NAME		BABY'S SEX	TIME OF BIRTH
PLACE OF BIRTH		OTHERS IN ATTENDANCE	
THIRD AND FOURTH STAGES	POSTPARTUM		FEEDING

Date   Birth

MOTHER'S NAME AND ADDRESS		SIGNIFICANT HISTORY	
G/P	SUPPORT PERSONS	BIRTH STORY	
MATERNAL AGE			

MEDICATIONS AND INTERVENTIONS	LENGTH OF LABOR STAGES	APGARS AND WEIGHT
	LACERATIONS/EPISIOTOMY	BIRTH POSITION

BABY'S NAME	BABY'S SEX	TIME OF BIRTH
PLACE OF BIRTH	OTHERS IN ATTENDANCE	

THIRD AND FOURTH STAGES	POSTPARTUM	FEEDING

Date   Birth

MOTHER'S NAME AND ADDRESS		SIGNIFICANT HISTORY	
G/P	SUPPORT PERSONS	BIRTH STORY	
MATERNAL AGE			

MEDICATIONS AND INTERVENTIONS	LENGTH OF LABOR STAGES	APGARS AND WEIGHT
	LACERATIONS/EPISIOTOMY	BIRTH POSITION

BABY'S NAME	BABY'S SEX	TIME OF BIRTH
PLACE OF BIRTH	OTHERS IN ATTENDANCE	

THIRD AND FOURTH STAGES	POSTPARTUM	FEEDING

Birth #   Date

MOTHER'S NAME AND ADDRESS		SIGNIFICANT HISTORY
G/P	SUPPORT PERSONS	BIRTH STORY
MATERNAL AGE		

MEDICATIONS AND INTERVENTIONS	LENGTH OF LABOR STAGES	APGARS AND WEIGHT
	LACERATIONS/EPISIOTOMY	BIRTH POSITION
BABY'S NAME	BABY'S SEX	TIME OF BIRTH
PLACE OF BIRTH	OTHERS IN ATTENDANCE	
THIRD AND FOURTH STAGES	POSTPARTUM	FEEDING

Birth #   Date

MOTHER'S NAME AND ADDRESS		SIGNIFICANT HISTORY
G/P	SUPPORT PERSONS	BIRTH STORY
MATERNAL AGE		

MEDICATIONS AND INTERVENTIONS	LENGTH OF LABOR STAGES	APGARS AND WEIGHT
	LACERATIONS/EPISIOTOMY	BIRTH POSITION
BABY'S NAME	BABY'S SEX	TIME OF BIRTH
PLACE OF BIRTH	OTHERS IN ATTENDANCE	
THIRD AND FOURTH STAGES	POSTPARTUM	FEEDING

# Stories To Remember

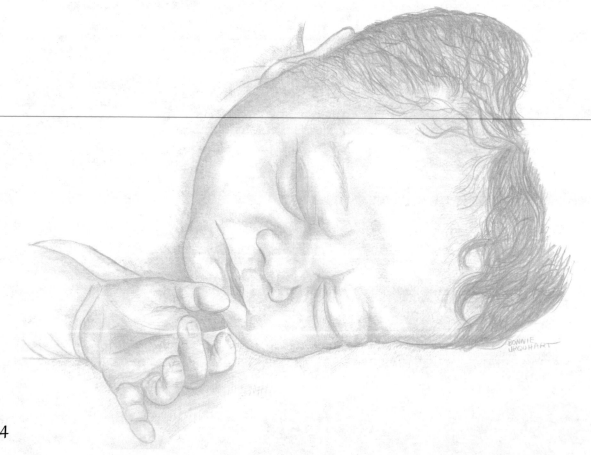

Date   Birth

MOTHER'S NAME AND ADDRESS		SIGNIFICANT HISTORY	
G/P	**SUPPORT PERSONS**	**BIRTH STORY**	
MATERNAL AGE			

MEDICATIONS AND INTERVENTIONS	LENGTH OF LABOR STAGES	APGARS AND WEIGHT
	LACERATIONS/EPISIOTOMY	BIRTH POSITION

BABY'S NAME	BABY'S SEX	TIME OF BIRTH
PLACE OF BIRTH	OTHERS IN ATTENDANCE	

THIRD AND FOURTH STAGES	POSTPARTUM	FEEDING

Date   Birth

MOTHER'S NAME AND ADDRESS		SIGNIFICANT HISTORY	
G/P	**SUPPORT PERSONS**	**BIRTH STORY**	
MATERNAL AGE			

MEDICATIONS AND INTERVENTIONS	LENGTH OF LABOR STAGES	APGARS AND WEIGHT
	LACERATIONS/EPISIOTOMY	BIRTH POSITION

BABY'S NAME	BABY'S SEX	TIME OF BIRTH
PLACE OF BIRTH	OTHERS IN ATTENDANCE	

THIRD AND FOURTH STAGES	POSTPARTUM	FEEDING

Birth
Date

MOTHER'S NAME AND ADDRESS		SIGNIFICANT HISTORY
G/P	SUPPORT PERSONS	BIRTH STORY
MATERNAL AGE		

MEDICATIONS AND INTERVENTIONS	LENGTH OF LABOR STAGES	APGARS AND WEIGHT
	LACERATIONS/EPISIOTOMY	BIRTH POSITION
BABY'S NAME	BABY'S SEX	TIME OF BIRTH
PLACE OF BIRTH	OTHERS IN ATTENDANCE	

THIRD AND FOURTH STAGES	POSTPARTUM	FEEDING

Birth
Date

MOTHER'S NAME AND ADDRESS		SIGNIFICANT HISTORY
G/P	SUPPORT PERSONS	BIRTH STORY
MATERNAL AGE		

MEDICATIONS AND INTERVENTIONS	LENGTH OF LABOR STAGES	APGARS AND WEIGHT
	LACERATIONS/EPISIOTOMY	BIRTH POSITION
BABY'S NAME	BABY'S SEX	TIME OF BIRTH
PLACE OF BIRTH	OTHERS IN ATTENDANCE	

THIRD AND FOURTH STAGES	POSTPARTUM	FEEDING

MOTHER'S NAME AND ADDRESS		SIGNIFICANT HISTORY	
G/P	SUPPORT PERSONS	BIRTH STORY	
MATERNAL AGE			
MEDICATIONS AND INTERVENTIONS	LENGTH OF LABOR STAGES		APGARS AND WEIGHT
	LACERATIONS/EPISIOTOMY		BIRTH POSITION
BABY'S NAME		BABY'S SEX	TIME OF BIRTH
PLACE OF BIRTH		OTHERS IN ATTENDANCE	
THIRD AND FOURTH STAGES	POSTPARTUM		FEEDING

MOTHER'S NAME AND ADDRESS		SIGNIFICANT HISTORY	
G/P	SUPPORT PERSONS	BIRTH STORY	
MATERNAL AGE			
MEDICATIONS AND INTERVENTIONS	LENGTH OF LABOR STAGES		APGARS AND WEIGHT
	LACERATIONS/EPISIOTOMY		BIRTH POSITION
BABY'S NAME		BABY'S SEX	TIME OF BIRTH
PLACE OF BIRTH		OTHERS IN ATTENDANCE	
THIRD AND FOURTH STAGES	POSTPARTUM		FEEDING

Birth #   Date

MOTHER'S NAME AND ADDRESS		SIGNIFICANT HISTORY	

G/P	SUPPORT PERSONS	BIRTH STORY	
MATERNAL AGE			

MEDICATIONS AND INTERVENTIONS	LENGTH OF LABOR STAGES	APGARS AND WEIGHT
	LACERATIONS/EPISIOTOMY	BIRTH POSITION

BABY'S NAME	BABY'S SEX	TIME OF BIRTH
PLACE OF BIRTH	OTHERS IN ATTENDANCE	

THIRD AND FOURTH STAGES	POSTPARTUM	FEEDING

Birth #   Date

MOTHER'S NAME AND ADDRESS		SIGNIFICANT HISTORY	

G/P	SUPPORT PERSONS	BIRTH STORY	
MATERNAL AGE			

MEDICATIONS AND INTERVENTIONS	LENGTH OF LABOR STAGES	APGARS AND WEIGHT
	LACERATIONS/EPISIOTOMY	BIRTH POSITION

BABY'S NAME	BABY'S SEX	TIME OF BIRTH
PLACE OF BIRTH	OTHERS IN ATTENDANCE	

THIRD AND FOURTH STAGES	POSTPARTUM	FEEDING

Date   **Birth #**

MOTHER'S NAME AND ADDRESS		SIGNIFICANT HISTORY
G/P	SUPPORT PERSONS	BIRTH STORY
MATERNAL AGE		

MEDICATIONS AND INTERVENTIONS	LENGTH OF LABOR STAGES	APGARS AND WEIGHT
	LACERATIONS/EPISIOTOMY	BIRTH POSITION
BABY'S NAME	BABY'S SEX	TIME OF BIRTH
PLACE OF BIRTH	OTHERS IN ATTENDANCE	
THIRD AND FOURTH STAGES	POSTPARTUM	FEEDING

Date   **Birth #**

MOTHER'S NAME AND ADDRESS		SIGNIFICANT HISTORY
G/P	SUPPORT PERSONS	BIRTH STORY
MATERNAL AGE		

MEDICATIONS AND INTERVENTIONS	LENGTH OF LABOR STAGES	APGARS AND WEIGHT
	LACERATIONS/EPISIOTOMY	BIRTH POSITION
BABY'S NAME	BABY'S SEX	TIME OF BIRTH
PLACE OF BIRTH	OTHERS IN ATTENDANCE	
THIRD AND FOURTH STAGES	POSTPARTUM	FEEDING

Birth

Date

MOTHER'S NAME AND ADDRESS			SIGNIFICANT HISTORY	
G/P	**SUPPORT PERSONS**		**BIRTH STORY**	
MATERNAL AGE				
MEDICATIONS AND INTERVENTIONS	**LENGTH OF LABOR STAGES**		**APGARS AND WEIGHT**	
	LACERATIONS/EPISIOTOMY		**BIRTH POSITION**	
BABY'S NAME		**BABY'S SEX**	**TIME OF BIRTH**	
PLACE OF BIRTH		**OTHERS IN ATTENDANCE**		
THIRD AND FOURTH STAGES	**POSTPARTUM**		**FEEDING**	

Birth

Date

MOTHER'S NAME AND ADDRESS			SIGNIFICANT HISTORY	
G/P	**SUPPORT PERSONS**		**BIRTH STORY**	
MATERNAL AGE				
MEDICATIONS AND INTERVENTIONS	**LENGTH OF LABOR STAGES**		**APGARS AND WEIGHT**	
	LACERATIONS/EPISIOTOMY		**BIRTH POSITION**	
BABY'S NAME		**BABY'S SEX**	**TIME OF BIRTH**	
PLACE OF BIRTH		**OTHERS IN ATTENDANCE**		
THIRD AND FOURTH STAGES	**POSTPARTUM**		**FEEDING**	

Date   Birth

MOTHER'S NAME AND ADDRESS		SIGNIFICANT HISTORY
G/P	**SUPPORT PERSONS**	**BIRTH STORY**
MATERNAL AGE		

MEDICATIONS AND INTERVENTIONS	LENGTH OF LABOR STAGES	APGARS AND WEIGHT
	LACERATIONS/EPISIOTOMY	BIRTH POSITION

BABY'S NAME	BABY'S SEX	TIME OF BIRTH
PLACE OF BIRTH	OTHERS IN ATTENDANCE	

THIRD AND FOURTH STAGES	POSTPARTUM	FEEDING

Date   Birth

MOTHER'S NAME AND ADDRESS		SIGNIFICANT HISTORY
G/P	**SUPPORT PERSONS**	**BIRTH STORY**
MATERNAL AGE		

MEDICATIONS AND INTERVENTIONS	LENGTH OF LABOR STAGES	APGARS AND WEIGHT
	LACERATIONS/EPISIOTOMY	BIRTH POSITION

BABY'S NAME	BABY'S SEX	TIME OF BIRTH
PLACE OF BIRTH	OTHERS IN ATTENDANCE	

THIRD AND FOURTH STAGES	POSTPARTUM	FEEDING

Birth #   Date

MOTHER'S NAME AND ADDRESS		SIGNIFICANT HISTORY	
G/P	SUPPORT PERSONS	BIRTH STORY	
MATERNAL AGE			

MEDICATIONS AND INTERVENTIONS	LENGTH OF LABOR STAGES	APGARS AND WEIGHT
	LACERATIONS/EPISIOTOMY	BIRTH POSITION

BABY'S NAME	BABY'S SEX	TIME OF BIRTH
PLACE OF BIRTH	OTHERS IN ATTENDANCE	

THIRD AND FOURTH STAGES	POSTPARTUM	FEEDING

Birth #   Date

MOTHER'S NAME AND ADDRESS		SIGNIFICANT HISTORY	
G/P	SUPPORT PERSONS	BIRTH STORY	
MATERNAL AGE			

MEDICATIONS AND INTERVENTIONS	LENGTH OF LABOR STAGES	APGARS AND WEIGHT
	LACERATIONS/EPISIOTOMY	BIRTH POSITION

BABY'S NAME	BABY'S SEX	TIME OF BIRTH
PLACE OF BIRTH	OTHERS IN ATTENDANCE	

THIRD AND FOURTH STAGES	POSTPARTUM	FEEDING

Date

Birth

MOTHER'S NAME AND ADDRESS	SIGNIFICANT HISTORY

G/P	SUPPORT PERSONS	BIRTH STORY
MATERNAL AGE		

MEDICATIONS AND INTERVENTIONS	LENGTH OF LABOR STAGES	APGARS AND WEIGHT
	LACERATIONS/EPISIOTOMY	BIRTH POSITION

BABY'S NAME	BABY'S SEX	TIME OF BIRTH

PLACE OF BIRTH	OTHERS IN ATTENDANCE	

THIRD AND FOURTH STAGES	POSTPARTUM	FEEDING

Date

Birth

MOTHER'S NAME AND ADDRESS	SIGNIFICANT HISTORY

G/P	SUPPORT PERSONS	BIRTH STORY
MATERNAL AGE		

MEDICATIONS AND INTERVENTIONS	LENGTH OF LABOR STAGES	APGARS AND WEIGHT
	LACERATIONS/EPISIOTOMY	BIRTH POSITION

BABY'S NAME	BABY'S SEX	TIME OF BIRTH

PLACE OF BIRTH	OTHERS IN ATTENDANCE	

THIRD AND FOURTH STAGES	POSTPARTUM	FEEDING

Birth #   Date

MOTHER'S NAME AND ADDRESS		SIGNIFICANT HISTORY	
G/P	**SUPPORT PERSONS**	**BIRTH STORY**	
MATERNAL AGE			

MEDICATIONS AND INTERVENTIONS	LENGTH OF LABOR STAGES	APGARS AND WEIGHT
	LACERATIONS/EPISIOTOMY	**BIRTH POSITION**

BABY'S NAME	BABY'S SEX	TIME OF BIRTH
PLACE OF BIRTH	**OTHERS IN ATTENDANCE**	

THIRD AND FOURTH STAGES	POSTPARTUM	FEEDING

Birth #   Date

MOTHER'S NAME AND ADDRESS		SIGNIFICANT HISTORY	
G/P	**SUPPORT PERSONS**	**BIRTH STORY**	
MATERNAL AGE			

MEDICATIONS AND INTERVENTIONS	LENGTH OF LABOR STAGES	APGARS AND WEIGHT
	LACERATIONS/EPISIOTOMY	**BIRTH POSITION**

BABY'S NAME	BABY'S SEX	TIME OF BIRTH
PLACE OF BIRTH	**OTHERS IN ATTENDANCE**	

THIRD AND FOURTH STAGES	POSTPARTUM	FEEDING

© Bonnie Urquhart 2003

Tales To Tell

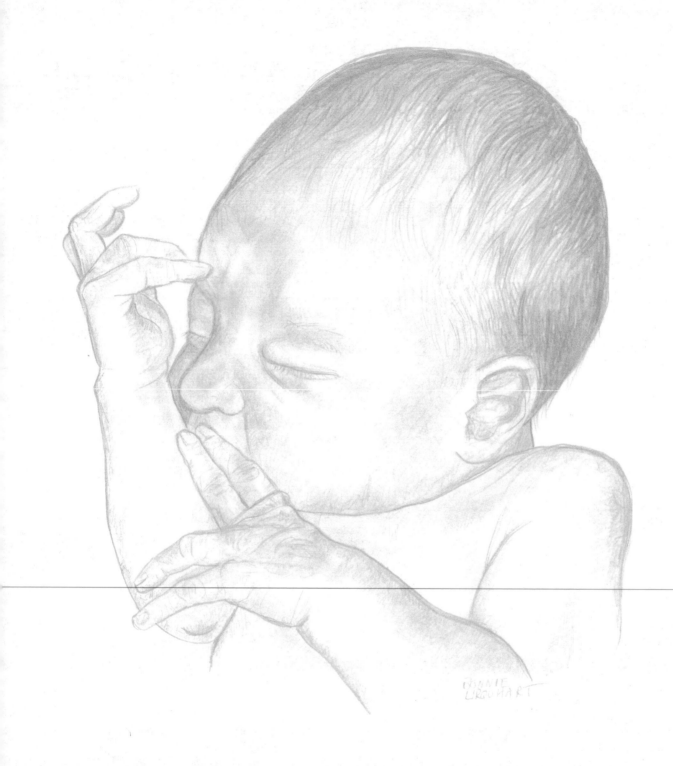

Gruenberg's Observation on Intuition

Intuition is a powerful tool for diagnosis and treatment, but
it can be confused with training, habit, worry, preference,
prejudice, or snap judgment.

Date   Birth

MOTHER'S NAME AND ADDRESS		SIGNIFICANT HISTORY
G/P	SUPPORT PERSONS	BIRTH STORY
MATERNAL AGE		

MEDICATIONS AND INTERVENTIONS	LENGTH OF LABOR STAGES	APGARS AND WEIGHT
	LACERATIONS/EPISIOTOMY	BIRTH POSITION

BABY'S NAME	BABY'S SEX	TIME OF BIRTH
PLACE OF BIRTH	OTHERS IN ATTENDANCE	

THIRD AND FOURTH STAGES	POSTPARTUM	FEEDING

Date   Birth

MOTHER'S NAME AND ADDRESS		SIGNIFICANT HISTORY
G/P	SUPPORT PERSONS	BIRTH STORY
MATERNAL AGE		

MEDICATIONS AND INTERVENTIONS	LENGTH OF LABOR STAGES	APGARS AND WEIGHT
	LACERATIONS/EPISIOTOMY	BIRTH POSITION

BABY'S NAME	BABY'S SEX	TIME OF BIRTH
PLACE OF BIRTH	OTHERS IN ATTENDANCE	

THIRD AND FOURTH STAGES	POSTPARTUM	FEEDING

Birth #   Date

MOTHER'S NAME AND ADDRESS		SIGNIFICANT HISTORY
G/P	SUPPORT PERSONS	BIRTH STORY
MATERNAL AGE		

MEDICATIONS AND INTERVENTIONS	LENGTH OF LABOR STAGES	APGARS AND WEIGHT
	LACERATIONS/EPISIOTOMY	BIRTH POSITION

BABY'S NAME	BABY'S SEX	TIME OF BIRTH
PLACE OF BIRTH	OTHERS IN ATTENDANCE	

THIRD AND FOURTH STAGES	POSTPARTUM	FEEDING

Birth #   Date

MOTHER'S NAME AND ADDRESS		SIGNIFICANT HISTORY
G/P	SUPPORT PERSONS	BIRTH STORY
MATERNAL AGE		

MEDICATIONS AND INTERVENTIONS	LENGTH OF LABOR STAGES	APGARS AND WEIGHT
	LACERATIONS/EPISIOTOMY	BIRTH POSITION

BABY'S NAME	BABY'S SEX	TIME OF BIRTH
PLACE OF BIRTH	OTHERS IN ATTENDANCE	

THIRD AND FOURTH STAGES	POSTPARTUM	FEEDING

Date

Birth

MOTHER'S NAME AND ADDRESS		SIGNIFICANT HISTORY		
G/P	SUPPORT PERSONS	BIRTH STORY		
MATERNAL AGE				
MEDICATIONS AND INTERVENTIONS	LENGTH OF LABOR STAGES		APGARS AND WEIGHT	
	LACERATIONS/EPISIOTOMY		BIRTH POSITION	
BABY'S NAME		BABY'S SEX	TIME OF BIRTH	
PLACE OF BIRTH		OTHERS IN ATTENDANCE		
THIRD AND FOURTH STAGES	POSTPARTUM		FEEDING	

Date

Birth

MOTHER'S NAME AND ADDRESS		SIGNIFICANT HISTORY		
G/P	SUPPORT PERSONS	BIRTH STORY		
MATERNAL AGE				
MEDICATIONS AND INTERVENTIONS	LENGTH OF LABOR STAGES		APGARS AND WEIGHT	
	LACERATIONS/EPISIOTOMY		BIRTH POSITION	
BABY'S NAME		BABY'S SEX	TIME OF BIRTH	
PLACE OF BIRTH		OTHERS IN ATTENDANCE		
THIRD AND FOURTH STAGES	POSTPARTUM		FEEDING	

Birth #   Date

MOTHER'S NAME AND ADDRESS		SIGNIFICANT HISTORY
G/P	SUPPORT PERSONS	BIRTH STORY
MATERNAL AGE		

MEDICATIONS AND INTERVENTIONS	LENGTH OF LABOR STAGES	APGARS AND WEIGHT
	LACERATIONS/EPISIOTOMY	BIRTH POSITION

BABY'S NAME	BABY'S SEX	TIME OF BIRTH
PLACE OF BIRTH	OTHERS IN ATTENDANCE	

THIRD AND FOURTH STAGES	POSTPARTUM	FEEDING

Birth #   Date

MOTHER'S NAME AND ADDRESS		SIGNIFICANT HISTORY
G/P	SUPPORT PERSONS	BIRTH STORY
MATERNAL AGE		

MEDICATIONS AND INTERVENTIONS	LENGTH OF LABOR STAGES	APGARS AND WEIGHT
	LACERATIONS/EPISIOTOMY	BIRTH POSITION

BABY'S NAME	BABY'S SEX	TIME OF BIRTH
PLACE OF BIRTH	OTHERS IN ATTENDANCE	

THIRD AND FOURTH STAGES	POSTPARTUM	FEEDING

Date   Birth

MOTHER'S NAME AND ADDRESS		SIGNIFICANT HISTORY
G/P	SUPPORT PERSONS	BIRTH STORY
MATERNAL AGE		

MEDICATIONS AND INTERVENTIONS	LENGTH OF LABOR STAGES	APGARS AND WEIGHT
	LACERATIONS/EPISIOTOMY	BIRTH POSITION

BABY'S NAME	BABY'S SEX	TIME OF BIRTH
PLACE OF BIRTH	OTHERS IN ATTENDANCE	

THIRD AND FOURTH STAGES	POSTPARTUM	FEEDING

Date   Birth

MOTHER'S NAME AND ADDRESS		SIGNIFICANT HISTORY
G/P	SUPPORT PERSONS	BIRTH STORY
MATERNAL AGE		

MEDICATIONS AND INTERVENTIONS	LENGTH OF LABOR STAGES	APGARS AND WEIGHT
	LACERATIONS/EPISIOTOMY	BIRTH POSITION

BABY'S NAME	BABY'S SEX	TIME OF BIRTH
PLACE OF BIRTH	OTHERS IN ATTENDANCE	

THIRD AND FOURTH STAGES	POSTPARTUM	FEEDING

Birth #   Date

MOTHER'S NAME AND ADDRESS		SIGNIFICANT HISTORY	

G/P	SUPPORT PERSONS	BIRTH STORY	
MATERNAL AGE			

MEDICATIONS AND INTERVENTIONS	LENGTH OF LABOR STAGES	APGARS AND WEIGHT
	LACERATIONS/EPISIOTOMY	BIRTH POSITION

BABY'S NAME	BABY'S SEX	TIME OF BIRTH
PLACE OF BIRTH	OTHERS IN ATTENDANCE	

THIRD AND FOURTH STAGES	POSTPARTUM	FEEDING

Birth #   Date

MOTHER'S NAME AND ADDRESS		SIGNIFICANT HISTORY	

G/P	SUPPORT PERSONS	BIRTH STORY	
MATERNAL AGE			

MEDICATIONS AND INTERVENTIONS	LENGTH OF LABOR STAGES	APGARS AND WEIGHT
	LACERATIONS/EPISIOTOMY	BIRTH POSITION

BABY'S NAME	BABY'S SEX	TIME OF BIRTH
PLACE OF BIRTH	OTHERS IN ATTENDANCE	

THIRD AND FOURTH STAGES	POSTPARTUM	FEEDING

Date   Birth

MOTHER'S NAME AND ADDRESS		SIGNIFICANT HISTORY	
G/P	SUPPORT PERSONS	BIRTH STORY	
MATERNAL AGE			
MEDICATIONS AND INTERVENTIONS	LENGTH OF LABOR STAGES	APGARS AND WEIGHT	
	LACERATIONS/EPISIOTOMY	BIRTH POSITION	
BABY'S NAME	BABY'S SEX	TIME OF BIRTH	
PLACE OF BIRTH	OTHERS IN ATTENDANCE		
THIRD AND FOURTH STAGES	POSTPARTUM	FEEDING	

Date   Birth

MOTHER'S NAME AND ADDRESS		SIGNIFICANT HISTORY	
G/P	SUPPORT PERSONS	BIRTH STORY	
MATERNAL AGE			
MEDICATIONS AND INTERVENTIONS	LENGTH OF LABOR STAGES	APGARS AND WEIGHT	
	LACERATIONS/EPISIOTOMY	BIRTH POSITION	
BABY'S NAME	BABY'S SEX	TIME OF BIRTH	
PLACE OF BIRTH	OTHERS IN ATTENDANCE		
THIRD AND FOURTH STAGES	POSTPARTUM	FEEDING	

Birth

Date

MOTHER'S NAME AND ADDRESS	SIGNIFICANT HISTORY

G/P	SUPPORT PERSONS	BIRTH STORY
MATERNAL AGE		

MEDICATIONS AND INTERVENTIONS	LENGTH OF LABOR STAGES	APGARS AND WEIGHT
	LACERATIONS/EPISIOTOMY	BIRTH POSITION

BABY'S NAME	BABY'S SEX	TIME OF BIRTH
PLACE OF BIRTH	OTHERS IN ATTENDANCE	

THIRD AND FOURTH STAGES	POSTPARTUM	FEEDING

Birth

Date

MOTHER'S NAME AND ADDRESS	SIGNIFICANT HISTORY

G/P	SUPPORT PERSONS	BIRTH STORY
MATERNAL AGE		

MEDICATIONS AND INTERVENTIONS	LENGTH OF LABOR STAGES	APGARS AND WEIGHT
	LACERATIONS/EPISIOTOMY	BIRTH POSITION

BABY'S NAME	BABY'S SEX	TIME OF BIRTH
PLACE OF BIRTH	OTHERS IN ATTENDANCE	

THIRD AND FOURTH STAGES	POSTPARTUM	FEEDING

Date   Birth

MOTHER'S NAME AND ADDRESS		SIGNIFICANT HISTORY
G/P	SUPPORT PERSONS	BIRTH STORY
MATERNAL AGE		

MEDICATIONS AND INTERVENTIONS	LENGTH OF LABOR STAGES	APGARS AND WEIGHT
	LACERATIONS/EPISIOTOMY	BIRTH POSITION
BABY'S NAME	BABY'S SEX	TIME OF BIRTH
PLACE OF BIRTH	OTHERS IN ATTENDANCE	

THIRD AND FOURTH STAGES	POSTPARTUM	FEEDING

Date   Birth

MOTHER'S NAME AND ADDRESS		SIGNIFICANT HISTORY
G/P	SUPPORT PERSONS	BIRTH STORY
MATERNAL AGE		

MEDICATIONS AND INTERVENTIONS	LENGTH OF LABOR STAGES	APGARS AND WEIGHT
	LACERATIONS/EPISIOTOMY	BIRTH POSITION
BABY'S NAME	BABY'S SEX	TIME OF BIRTH
PLACE OF BIRTH	OTHERS IN ATTENDANCE	

THIRD AND FOURTH STAGES	POSTPARTUM	FEEDING

Birth #   Date

MOTHER'S NAME AND ADDRESS		SIGNIFICANT HISTORY	
G/P	**SUPPORT PERSONS**	**BIRTH STORY**	
MATERNAL AGE			

MEDICATIONS AND INTERVENTIONS	LENGTH OF LABOR STAGES	APGARS AND WEIGHT
	LACERATIONS/EPISIOTOMY	BIRTH POSITION

BABY'S NAME	BABY'S SEX	TIME OF BIRTH
PLACE OF BIRTH	OTHERS IN ATTENDANCE	

THIRD AND FOURTH STAGES	POSTPARTUM	FEEDING

Birth #   Date

MOTHER'S NAME AND ADDRESS		SIGNIFICANT HISTORY	
G/P	**SUPPORT PERSONS**	**BIRTH STORY**	
MATERNAL AGE			

MEDICATIONS AND INTERVENTIONS	LENGTH OF LABOR STAGES	APGARS AND WEIGHT
	LACERATIONS/EPISIOTOMY	BIRTH POSITION

BABY'S NAME	BABY'S SEX	TIME OF BIRTH
PLACE OF BIRTH	OTHERS IN ATTENDANCE	

THIRD AND FOURTH STAGES	POSTPARTUM	FEEDING

Notes

Cesareans

Date   Birth

MOTHER'S NAME AND ADDRESS	SIGNIFICANT HISTORY

G/P	SUPPORT PERSONS	BIRTH STORY
MATERNAL AGE		

MEDICATIONS AND INTERVENTIONS	LENGTH OF LABOR STAGES	APGARS AND WEIGHT
	LACERATIONS/EPISIOTOMY	BIRTH POSITION

BABY'S NAME	BABY'S SEX	TIME OF BIRTH

PLACE OF BIRTH	OTHERS IN ATTENDANCE

THIRD AND FOURTH STAGES	POSTPARTUM	FEEDING

Date   Birth

MOTHER'S NAME AND ADDRESS	SIGNIFICANT HISTORY

G/P	SUPPORT PERSONS	BIRTH STORY
MATERNAL AGE		

MEDICATIONS AND INTERVENTIONS	LENGTH OF LABOR STAGES	APGARS AND WEIGHT
	LACERATIONS/EPISIOTOMY	BIRTH POSITION

BABY'S NAME	BABY'S SEX	TIME OF BIRTH

PLACE OF BIRTH	OTHERS IN ATTENDANCE

THIRD AND FOURTH STAGES	POSTPARTUM	FEEDING

Cesareans

Birth #   Date

MOTHER'S NAME AND ADDRESS		SIGNIFICANT HISTORY
G/P	SUPPORT PERSONS	BIRTH STORY
MATERNAL AGE		

MEDICATIONS AND INTERVENTIONS	LENGTH OF LABOR STAGES	APGARS AND WEIGHT
	LACERATIONS/EPISIOTOMY	BIRTH POSITION
BABY'S NAME	BABY'S SEX	TIME OF BIRTH
PLACE OF BIRTH	OTHERS IN ATTENDANCE	

THIRD AND FOURTH STAGES	POSTPARTUM	FEEDING

Birth #   Date

MOTHER'S NAME AND ADDRESS		SIGNIFICANT HISTORY
G/P	SUPPORT PERSONS	BIRTH STORY
MATERNAL AGE		

MEDICATIONS AND INTERVENTIONS	LENGTH OF LABOR STAGES	APGARS AND WEIGHT
	LACERATIONS/EPISIOTOMY	BIRTH POSITION
BABY'S NAME	BABY'S SEX	TIME OF BIRTH
PLACE OF BIRTH	OTHERS IN ATTENDANCE	

THIRD AND FOURTH STAGES	POSTPARTUM	FEEDING

Cesareans

Date _____ Birth # _____

MOTHER'S NAME AND ADDRESS	SIGNIFICANT HISTORY

G/P	SUPPORT PERSONS	BIRTH STORY
MATERNAL AGE		

MEDICATIONS AND INTERVENTIONS	LENGTH OF LABOR STAGES	APGARS AND WEIGHT
	LACERATIONS/EPISIOTOMY	BIRTH POSITION

BABY'S NAME	BABY'S SEX	TIME OF BIRTH
PLACE OF BIRTH	OTHERS IN ATTENDANCE	

THIRD AND FOURTH STAGES	POSTPARTUM	FEEDING

Date _____ Birth # _____

MOTHER'S NAME AND ADDRESS	SIGNIFICANT HISTORY

G/P	SUPPORT PERSONS	BIRTH STORY
MATERNAL AGE		

MEDICATIONS AND INTERVENTIONS	LENGTH OF LABOR STAGES	APGARS AND WEIGHT
	LACERATIONS/EPISIOTOMY	BIRTH POSITION

BABY'S NAME	BABY'S SEX	TIME OF BIRTH
PLACE OF BIRTH	OTHERS IN ATTENDANCE	

THIRD AND FOURTH STAGES	POSTPARTUM	FEEDING

Cesareans

Birth #   Date

MOTHER'S NAME AND ADDRESS		SIGNIFICANT HISTORY

G/P	SUPPORT PERSONS	BIRTH STORY
MATERNAL AGE		

MEDICATIONS AND INTERVENTIONS	LENGTH OF LABOR STAGES	APGARS AND WEIGHT
	LACERATIONS/EPISIOTOMY	BIRTH POSITION

BABY'S NAME	BABY'S SEX	TIME OF BIRTH
PLACE OF BIRTH	OTHERS IN ATTENDANCE	

THIRD AND FOURTH STAGES	POSTPARTUM	FEEDING

Birth #   Date

MOTHER'S NAME AND ADDRESS		SIGNIFICANT HISTORY

G/P	SUPPORT PERSONS	BIRTH STORY
MATERNAL AGE		

MEDICATIONS AND INTERVENTIONS	LENGTH OF LABOR STAGES	APGARS AND WEIGHT
	LACERATIONS/EPISIOTOMY	BIRTH POSITION

BABY'S NAME	BABY'S SEX	TIME OF BIRTH
PLACE OF BIRTH	OTHERS IN ATTENDANCE	

THIRD AND FOURTH STAGES	POSTPARTUM	FEEDING

Cesareans

Date   Birth

MOTHER'S NAME AND ADDRESS	SIGNIFICANT HISTORY

G/P	SUPPORT PERSONS	BIRTH STORY
MATERNAL AGE		

MEDICATIONS AND INTERVENTIONS	LENGTH OF LABOR STAGES	APGARS AND WEIGHT
	LACERATIONS/EPISIOTOMY	BIRTH POSITION

BABY'S NAME	BABY'S SEX	TIME OF BIRTH

PLACE OF BIRTH	OTHERS IN ATTENDANCE

THIRD AND FOURTH STAGES	POSTPARTUM	FEEDING

Date   Birth

MOTHER'S NAME AND ADDRESS	SIGNIFICANT HISTORY

G/P	SUPPORT PERSONS	BIRTH STORY
MATERNAL AGE		

MEDICATIONS AND INTERVENTIONS	LENGTH OF LABOR STAGES	APGARS AND WEIGHT
	LACERATIONS/EPISIOTOMY	BIRTH POSITION

BABY'S NAME	BABY'S SEX	TIME OF BIRTH

PLACE OF BIRTH	OTHERS IN ATTENDANCE

THIRD AND FOURTH STAGES	POSTPARTUM	FEEDING

Cesareans

Birth #   Date

MOTHER'S NAME AND ADDRESS	SIGNIFICANT HISTORY

G/P	SUPPORT PERSONS	BIRTH STORY
MATERNAL AGE		

MEDICATIONS AND INTERVENTIONS	LENGTH OF LABOR STAGES	APGARS AND WEIGHT
	LACERATIONS/EPISIOTOMY	BIRTH POSITION

BABY'S NAME	BABY'S SEX	TIME OF BIRTH

PLACE OF BIRTH	OTHERS IN ATTENDANCE

THIRD AND FOURTH STAGES	POSTPARTUM	FEEDING

Birth #   Date

MOTHER'S NAME AND ADDRESS	SIGNIFICANT HISTORY

G/P	SUPPORT PERSONS	BIRTH STORY
MATERNAL AGE		

MEDICATIONS AND INTERVENTIONS	LENGTH OF LABOR STAGES	APGARS AND WEIGHT
	LACERATIONS/EPISIOTOMY	BIRTH POSITION

BABY'S NAME	BABY'S SEX	TIME OF BIRTH

PLACE OF BIRTH	OTHERS IN ATTENDANCE

THIRD AND FOURTH STAGES	POSTPARTUM	FEEDING

Date   Birth

MOTHER'S NAME AND ADDRESS	SIGNIFICANT HISTORY

G/P	SUPPORT PERSONS	BIRTH STORY
MATERNAL AGE		

MEDICATIONS AND INTERVENTIONS	LENGTH OF LABOR STAGES	APGARS AND WEIGHT
	LACERATIONS/EPISIOTOMY	BIRTH POSITION

BABY'S NAME	BABY'S SEX	TIME OF BIRTH

PLACE OF BIRTH	OTHERS IN ATTENDANCE	

THIRD AND FOURTH STAGES	POSTPARTUM	FEEDING

Date   Birth

MOTHER'S NAME AND ADDRESS	SIGNIFICANT HISTORY

G/P	SUPPORT PERSONS	BIRTH STORY
MATERNAL AGE		

MEDICATIONS AND INTERVENTIONS	LENGTH OF LABOR STAGES	APGARS AND WEIGHT
	LACERATIONS/EPISIOTOMY	BIRTH POSITION

BABY'S NAME	BABY'S SEX	TIME OF BIRTH

PLACE OF BIRTH	OTHERS IN ATTENDANCE	

THIRD AND FOURTH STAGES	POSTPARTUM	FEEDING

Cesareans

Birth #   Date

MOTHER'S NAME AND ADDRESS		SIGNIFICANT HISTORY

G/P	SUPPORT PERSONS	BIRTH STORY
MATERNAL AGE		

MEDICATIONS AND INTERVENTIONS	LENGTH OF LABOR STAGES	APGARS AND WEIGHT
	LACERATIONS/EPISIOTOMY	BIRTH POSITION

BABY'S NAME	BABY'S SEX	TIME OF BIRTH

PLACE OF BIRTH	OTHERS IN ATTENDANCE	

THIRD AND FOURTH STAGES	POSTPARTUM	FEEDING

Birth #   Date

MOTHER'S NAME AND ADDRESS		SIGNIFICANT HISTORY

G/P	SUPPORT PERSONS	BIRTH STORY
MATERNAL AGE		

MEDICATIONS AND INTERVENTIONS	LENGTH OF LABOR STAGES	APGARS AND WEIGHT
	LACERATIONS/EPISIOTOMY	BIRTH POSITION

BABY'S NAME	BABY'S SEX	TIME OF BIRTH

PLACE OF BIRTH	OTHERS IN ATTENDANCE	

THIRD AND FOURTH STAGES	POSTPARTUM	FEEDING

Cesareans

Date   Birth

MOTHER'S NAME AND ADDRESS	SIGNIFICANT HISTORY

G/P	SUPPORT PERSONS	BIRTH STORY
MATERNAL AGE		

MEDICATIONS AND INTERVENTIONS	LENGTH OF LABOR STAGES	APGARS AND WEIGHT
	LACERATIONS/EPISIOTOMY	BIRTH POSITION

BABY'S NAME	BABY'S SEX	TIME OF BIRTH

PLACE OF BIRTH	OTHERS IN ATTENDANCE	

THIRD AND FOURTH STAGES	POSTPARTUM	FEEDING

Date   Birth

MOTHER'S NAME AND ADDRESS	SIGNIFICANT HISTORY

G/P	SUPPORT PERSONS	BIRTH STORY
MATERNAL AGE		

MEDICATIONS AND INTERVENTIONS	LENGTH OF LABOR STAGES	APGARS AND WEIGHT
	LACERATIONS/EPISIOTOMY	BIRTH POSITION

BABY'S NAME	BABY'S SEX	TIME OF BIRTH

PLACE OF BIRTH	OTHERS IN ATTENDANCE	

THIRD AND FOURTH STAGES	POSTPARTUM	FEEDING

Cesareans

Birth #   Date

MOTHER'S NAME AND ADDRESS	SIGNIFICANT HISTORY

G/P	SUPPORT PERSONS	BIRTH STORY
MATERNAL AGE		

MEDICATIONS AND INTERVENTIONS	LENGTH OF LABOR STAGES	APGARS AND WEIGHT
	LACERATIONS/EPISIOTOMY	BIRTH POSITION

BABY'S NAME	BABY'S SEX	TIME OF BIRTH

PLACE OF BIRTH	OTHERS IN ATTENDANCE

THIRD AND FOURTH STAGES	POSTPARTUM	FEEDING

Birth #   Date

MOTHER'S NAME AND ADDRESS	SIGNIFICANT HISTORY

G/P	SUPPORT PERSONS	BIRTH STORY
MATERNAL AGE		

MEDICATIONS AND INTERVENTIONS	LENGTH OF LABOR STAGES	APGARS AND WEIGHT
	LACERATIONS/EPISIOTOMY	BIRTH POSITION

BABY'S NAME	BABY'S SEX	TIME OF BIRTH

PLACE OF BIRTH	OTHERS IN ATTENDANCE

THIRD AND FOURTH STAGES	POSTPARTUM	FEEDING

Notes

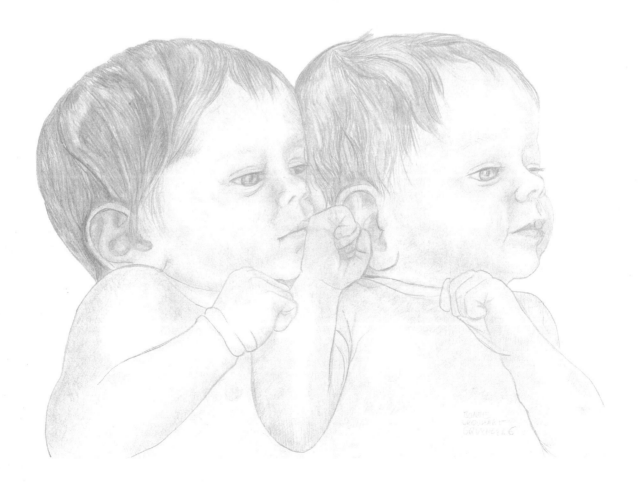

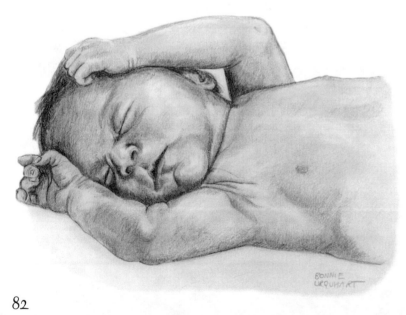

Gruenberg's Intervention Contention

Unnecessary intervention can be life-threatening. Necessary intervention can be life-saving.

Contact Information

Contact Information

Contact Information

NEUROMUSCULAR MATURITY

SCORE	-1	0	1	2	3	4	5
Posture							
Square Window (wrist)	>90°	90°	60°	45°	30°	0°	
Arm Recoil		180°	140–180°	110–140°	90–110°	<90°	
Popliteal Angle	180°	160°	140°	120°	100°	90°	<90°
Scarf Sign	Neck	Axillary line	Nipple	Xiphoid	Nipple	Axillary line	
Heel to Ear							

PHYSICAL MATURITY

	-1	0	1	2	3	4	5
Skin	Sticky, friable, transparent	Gelatinous, red, translucent	Smooth, pink; visible veins	Superficial peeling or rash; few veins	Cracking, pale areas; rare veins	Parchment, deep cracking; no veins	Leathery, cracked, wrinkled
Lanugo	None	Sparse	Abundant	Thinning	Bald areas	Mostly bald	
Plantar Surface	Heel-toe 40–50 mm (<40 mm: -2)	Heel-toe >50 mm; no crease	Faint red marks	Anterior transverse crease only	Creases anterior $^2/_3$	Creases over sole	
Breast	Imperceptible	Barely perceptible	Flat areola, no bud	Stippled areola, 1–2 mm bud	Raised areola, 3–4 mm bud	Full areola, 5–10 mm bud	
Eye & Ear	Lids fused loosely (fused tightly: -2)	Lids open; pinna flat, stays folded	Slightly curved pinna; soft; slow recoil	Well-curved pinna; soft, but ready recoil	Pinna formed and firm; instant recoil	Thick cartilage; ear stiff	
Genitals (male)	Scrotum flat, smooth	Scrotum empty, faint rugae	Testes in upper canal, rare rugae	Testes descending, few rugae	Testes down, good rugae	Testes pendulous, deep rugae	
Genitals (female)	Clitoris prominent, labia flat	Clitoris prominent, small labia minora	Clitoris prominent, enlarging minora	Majora and minora equally prominent	Majora large, minora small	Majora cover clitoris and minora	
TOTALS							

MATURITY RATING

TOTAL SCORE	-10	-5	0	5	10	15	20	25	30	35	40	45	50
WEEKS	20	22	24	26	28	30	32	34	36	38	40	42	44

LMP-EDD Chart

		1	2	3	4	5	6	7	8	9	10	11	12	13	14	15	16	17	18	19	20	21	22	23	24	25	26	27	28	29	30	31
LMP	JAN	1	2	3	4	5	6	7	8	9	10	11	12	13	14	15	16	17	18	19	20	21	22	23	24	25	26	27	28	29	30	31
EDD	OCT	8	9	10	11	12	13	14	15	16	17	18	19	20	21	22	23	24	25	26	27	28	29	30	31	1	2	3	4	5	6	7
LMP	FEB	1	2	3	4	5	6	7	8	9	10	11	12	13	14	15	16	17	18	19	20	21	22	23	24	25	26	27	28	**29†**		
EDD	NOV	8	9	10	11	12	13	14	15	16	17	18	19	20	21	22	23	24	25	26	27	28	29	30	1	2	3	4	5	**6†**		
LMP	MAR	1	2	3	4	5	6	7	8	9	10	11	12	13	14	15	16	17	18	19	20	21	22	23	24	25	26	27	28	29	30	31
EDD	DEC	6	7	8	9	10	11	12	13	14	15	16	17	18	19	20	21	22	23	24	25	26	27	28	29	30	31	1	2	3	4	5
LMP	APR	1	2	3	4	5	6	7	8	9	10	11	12	13	14	15	16	17	18	19	20	21	22	23	24	25	26	27	28	29	30	
EDD	JAN	6	7	8	9	10	11	12	13	14	15	16	17	18	19	20	21	22	23	24	25	26	27	28	29	30	31	1	2	3	4	
LMP	MAY	1	2	3	4	5	6	7	8	9	10	11	12	13	14	15	16	17	18	19	20	21	22	23	24	25	26	27	28	29	30	31
EDD	FEB	5	6	7	8	9	10	11	12	13	14	15	16	17	18	19	20	21	22	23	24	25	26	27	28	1	2	3	4	5	6	7
LMP	JUN	1	2	3	4	5	6	7	8	9	10	11	12	13	14	15	16	17	18	19	20	21	22	23	24	25	26	27	28	29	30	
EDD	MAR	8	9	10	11	12	13	14	15	16	17	18	19	20	21	22	23	24	25	26	27	28	29	30	31	1	2	3	4	5	6	
LMP	JUL	1	2	3	4	5	6	7	8	9	10	11	12	13	14	15	16	17	18	19	20	21	22	23	24	25	26	27	28	29	30	31
EDD	APR	7	8	9	10	11	12	13	14	15	16	17	18	19	20	21	22	23	24	25	26	27	28	29	30	1	2	3	4	5	6	7
LMP	AUG	1	2	3	4	5	6	7	8	9	10	11	12	13	14	15	16	17	18	19	20	21	22	23	24	25	26	27	28	29	30	31
EDD	MAY	8	9	10	11	12	13	14	15	16	17	18	19	20	21	22	23	24	25	26	27	28	29	30	31	1	2	3	4	5	6	7
LMP	SEP	1	2	3	4	5	6	7	8	9	10	11	12	13	14	15	16	17	18	19	20	21	22	23	24	25	26	27	28	29	30	
EDD	JUN	8	9	10	11	12	13	14	15	16	17	18	19	20	21	22	23	24	25	26	27	28	29	30	1	2	3	4	5	6	7	
LMP	OCT	1	2	3	4	5	6	7	8	9	10	11	12	13	14	15	16	17	18	19	20	21	22	23	24	25	26	27	28	29	30	31
EDD	JUL	8	9	10	11	12	13	14	15	16	17	18	19	20	21	22	23	24	25	26	27	28	29	30	31	1	2	3	4	5	6	7
LMP	NOV	1	2	3	4	5	6	7	8	9	10	11	12	13	14	15	16	17	18	19	20	21	22	23	24	25	26	27	28	29	30	
EDD	AUG	8	9	10	11	12	13	14	15	16	17	18	19	20	21	22	23	24	25	26	27	28	29	30	31	1	2	3	4	5	6	
LMP	DEC	1	2	3	4	5	6	7	8	9	10	11	12	13	14	15	16	17	18	19	20	21	22	23	24	25	26	27	28	29	30	31
EDD	SEP	7	8	9	10	11	12	13	14	15	16	17	18	19	20	21	22	23	24	25	26	27	28	29	30	1	2	3	4	5	6	7

†Add 1 to each subsequent LMP and EDD in leap years.

Pounds & Ounces to Grams

oz \ lb	1	2	3	4	5	6	7	8	9	10
0	454	907	1361	1814	2268	2722	3175	3629	4082	4536
1	482	936	1389	1843	2296	2750	3203	3657	4111	4564
2	510	964	1417	1871	2325	2778	3232	3685	4139	4593
3	539	992	1446	1899	2353	2807	3260	3714	4167	4621
4	567	1021	1474	1928	2381	2835	3289	3742	4196	4649
5	595	1049	1503	1956	2410	2863	3317	3770	4224	4678
6	624	1077	1531	1984	2438	2892	3345	3799	4252	4706
7	652	1106	1559	2013	2466	2920	3374	3827	4281	4734
8	680	1134	1588	2041	2495	2948	3402	3856	4309	4763
9	709	1162	1616	2070	2523	2977	3430	3884	4337	4791
10	737	1191	1644	2098	2551	3005	3459	3912	4366	4819
11	765	1219	1673	2126	2580	3033	3487	3941	4394	4848
12	794	1247	1701	2155	2608	3062	3515	3969	4423	4876
13	822	1276	1729	2183	2637	3090	3544	3997	4451	4904
14	850	1304	1758	2211	2665	3118	3572	4026	4479	4933
15	879	1332	1786	2240	2693	3147	3600	4054	4508	4961

1 lb = 453.6 g; 1 oz = 28.4 g.

Inches to Centimeters

in	1	2	3	4	5	6	7	8	9	10
cm	2.54	5.08	7.62	10.16	12.70	15.24	17.78	20.32	22.86	25.40
in	11	12	13	14	15	16	17	18	19	20
cm	27.94	30.48	33.02	35.56	38.10	40.64	43.18	45.72	48.26	50.80
in	21	22	23	24	25	26	27	28	29	30
cm	53.34	55.88	58.42	60.96	63.50	66.04	68.58	71.12	73.66	76.20

Bishop Score

Pts.	Dilation	Effacement	Station	Position	Consistency	Adjustments	
						+1 point	−1 point
0	Closed	0–30%	-3	Posterior	Firm	• Preeclampsia	• Postdates
1	1–2 cm	40–50%	-2	Mid	Medium	• Each previous vaginal delivery	• Nulliparity
2	3–4 cm	60–80%	-1, 0	Anterior	Soft		• Premature/prolonged ROM
3	5+ cm	>80%	+1, +2, +3				

Birth Weight & Gestational Age

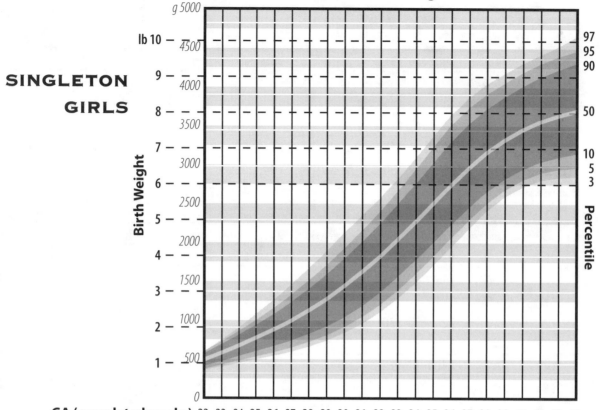

SINGLETON GIRLS

Birth Weight

Percentile

GA (completed weeks) 22 23 24 25 26 27 28 29 30 31 32 33 34 35 36 37 38 39 40 41 42 43

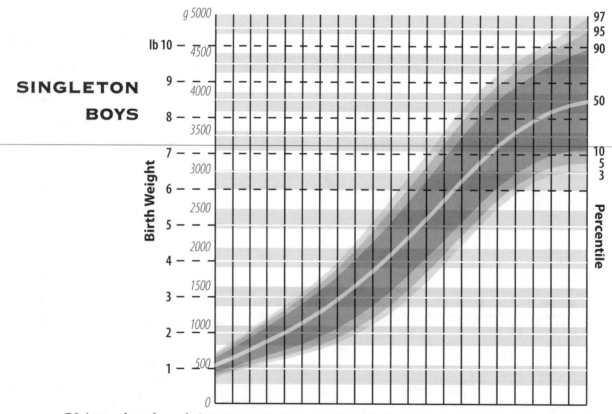

SINGLETON BOYS

Birth Weight

Percentile

GA (completed weeks) 22 23 24 25 26 27 28 29 30 31 32 33 34 35 36 37 38 39 40 41 42 43

 Index

3RD-DEGREE LACERATIONS

BIRTH NUMBERS	COMMENTS

4TH-DEGREE LACERATIONS

BIRTH NUMBERS	COMMENTS

APGARS BELOW 6 AT 5 MIN

BIRTH NUMBERS	COMMENTS

DEMISE

BIRTH NUMBERS	COMMENTS

ECLAMPSIA

BIRTH NUMBERS	COMMENTS

Index

EPISIOTOMIES

BIRTH NUMBERS	COMMENTS

HEMORRHAGE

BIRTH NUMBERS	COMMENTS

LABORS THAT WENT TO C/S

BIRTH NUMBERS	COMMENTS

LARGE FOR GESTATIONAL AGE

BIRTH NUMBERS	COMMENTS

MALPRESENTATIONS

BIRTH NUMBERS	COMMENTS

 Index

PREECLAMPSIA

BIRTH NUMBERS

COMMENTS

PRETERM DELIVERY

BIRTH NUMBERS

COMMENTS

SHOULDER DYSTOCIA

BIRTH NUMBERS

COMMENTS

SMALL FOR GESTATIONAL AGE

BIRTH NUMBERS

COMMENTS

TRANSFERS FROM HOME OR BIRTH CENTER TO HOSPITAL

BIRTH NUMBERS

COMMENTS

Index

TWINS

BIRTH NUMBERS	COMMENTS

VBAC

BIRTH NUMBERS	COMMENTS

BIRTH NUMBERS	COMMENTS

BIRTH NUMBERS	COMMENTS

BIRTH NUMBERS	COMMENTS

About the Author

Bonnie Urquhart Gruenberg is a certified nurse-midwife with an MSN from the University of Pennsylvania. Her midwifery experience has included births at home and in tertiary hospitals, and she has worked variously as an EMT, as a paramedic, and as a maternity nurse.

Bonnie has been published on diverse topics in professional journals and elsewhere. Her most recent book, *Birth Emergency Skills Training: Manual for Out-of-Hospital Midwives*, serves as a unique resource for birth attendants. It is also the backbone of the innovative Birth Emergency Skills Training (BEST) course, offered online through Aviva Institute for CME credit. Her *Essentials of Prehospital Maternity Care* (Prentice Hall, 2005) is the only book on the market written for EMS personnel who seek to improve their management of obstetrical emergencies. *Hoofprints in the Sand: Wild Horses of the Atlantic Coast* (Eclipse Press, 2002) is a hardcover volume featuring her text and photographs. She is a prize-winning artist and photographer who specializes in horses and infants, and she is the owner of Birth Guru Publications.

She lives in Duncannon, Pennsylvania, with her husband, Alex. She has two grown sons, Keith and Mark Bryan Scianna, and an amazing Connemara gelding named Fancy, also known as The Pone.

Great Deal from Birth Guru

Buy any three items, get a fourth FREE!

(Lowest price prevails. Ask about quantity discounts for resellers and groups .)

A Midwife's Journal: Birth Log and Memory Book

Contains provisions for recording 100 vaginal births and 20 cesareans, a section for addresses and telephone numbers, a variety of useful tables and charts, and plenty of space for notes and anecdotes. Designed to endure years of heavy use.

Paperback • 96 pages • 11 x 8.5 x 0.7 in
ISBN 13: 978-0-9790020-2-1 • ISBN 10: 0-9790020-2-8 • $18.99

Birth Emergency Skills Training

The last word on managing obstetrical emergencies for out-of-hospital midwives. With 121 black-and-white illustrations; 33 tables; abundant references; and a wealth of mnemonics, reminders, tips, and points to consider.

Paperback • 310 pages • 10 x 7 x 0.7 in
ISBN 13: 978-0-9790020-0-7 • ISBN 10: 0-9790020-0-1 • **$36.00**

BEST on CD-ROM

The full text of the groundbreaking book— plus FULL-COLOR ILLUSTRATIONS—in two popular e-book formats for use on desktop or notebook computers (PC and Mac) and a variety of hand-held devices.

Includes many informative and memorable POWERPOINTS used in the BEST course and keyed to the book. Nothing comparable can be found at twice the price.

ISBN 10: 0-9790020-1-X • ISBN 13: 978-0-9790020-1-4 • **$55.00**

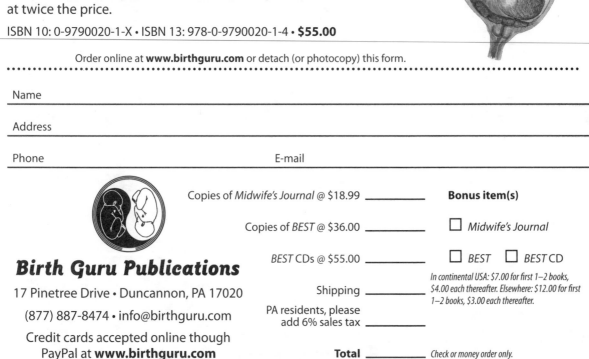